Activity Book

Deborah Roberts
Shahbano Bilgrami
Sue Cowley

OXFORD
UNIVERSITY PRESS

Contents

Amazing animals

In this topic, learners are encouraged to:

- explore the concept of zero
- recognize and follow numbers 1 to 10 in order
- talk and ask questions about animals and their babies
- join in with rhymes and songs
- identify animals' homes.

Teachers will also help learners to:

- hold a pencil and write numbers and letters with control
- explore and retell stories about pets and animals
- count sounds
- respond to opposite words such as 'slow/fast'
- count in sets and say if the 'total' is the same
- talk about growing up and memories.

Animal life

a Name the animals you know.

b Listen to your teacher and count the animals.

c Find an animal with a stripy pattern.

d Sing What animal is this?.

At home

Using online resources, go on a virtual zoo 'visit' with your child.

In these sessions, children will also: name zoo animals and young, learn about habitats, identify animal markings, patterns and footprints, make footprints. → TG pp. 100–103

a Trace the numbers.

b How many legs do the animals have? Draw lines to match with the numbers.

At home

Help your child count how many legs different toys have; play at moving around like animals with different numbers of legs.

In this session, children will also: count animals' legs and sort them into sets, explore animal sizes, move like different animals. → TG pp. 100–103

a Find the empty bottle.

b Circle the full bowl.

c Draw a line to match the full bowl and the full bottle.

In this session, children will also: find out what zoo animals eat, compare containers, measure out food and drink. → TG pp. 100–103

At home

Help your child fill bottles up with different amounts of water; ask which bottle has more/most.

a Find the pictures with water.

b Circle the picture that shows how people wash.

At home

Talk to your child about how to keep clean; remind them about washing their hands, clothes and bodies.

In this session, children will also: find out how animals keep clean, talk about keeping themselves clean, play with bubble bath, make bubble prints. → TG pp. 100–103

Babies, babies

a Find the real pet.

b Look. What is the biggest toy?

c Count the fish.

d Find the pet carrier.

At home

Print and/or cut out pictures of animals and their babies, then help your child match the baby to its parent.

In this session, children will also: name pets, find out about baby animals, paint and talk about their own pets. → TG pp. 104–106

Babies, babies

a Count the babies in the pictures.

b Trace the line to help the duckling.

c Colour the duckling and the ducks.

At home

Help your child name different ways in which you look after them.

In this session, children will also: learn how animals care for babies, practise tracing and drawing lines, meet a real pet, sing an animal action song. → TG pp. 104–106

a Look. Which is your favourite pet?

b Find the vet.

c Count the pets.

In this session, children will also: find out about vets, role play going to the vets, make new rhyming words, match boxes and toys by size. → TG pp. 104–106

At home

Go on a walk and look out for pets such as cats. Ask your child how owners care for their pets.

a Count the babies.

b Draw beds for the babies to sleep in.

At home

Go outside with your child and talk about any animals you see signs of; talk about how we care for these animals.

In this session, children will also: learn the word 'equal', make sets to match number cards, find out about homes for pets, use their hand to measure things. → TG pp. 104–106

a Colour the pet.

b Draw lines to match each animal to its home.

At home

Talk with your child about what animals do if they are frightened; create a den together using sheets or blankets indoors or using branches outdoors.

In this session, children will also: compare pets to wild animals, help care for animals nearby, pretend to be a wild animal, vote for favourite pets. → TG pp. 104–106

Animal fun!

Engage

a Look. What is Ms Zara doing?

b Count the children dressing up.

c Find the costumes. Which is your favourite?

d Chant Fast and slow.

In these sessions, children will also: make masks, dress up and move like animals, recall and read animal stories, start counting beyond 10. → TG pp. 107–109

At home

Encourage your child to act out a favourite animal-themed story.

a Find the animals which move slowly.

b Tick (✓) the biggest.

c Cross (✗) the smallest.

At home

Read an animal story to your child; talk about the size and speed of the animal(s) in the stories, relative to you.

In this session, children will also: compare fast and slow animals, move to a beat, make an obstacle course, sort objects into groups. → TG pp. 107–109

a Count the dots in each picture.

b Join the dots.

c Colour the animals.

At home

Cook with your child and notice opposites as you cook: a big/small spoon, wet/dry and soft/hard textures.

In this session, children will also: compare animal sizes, listen to an animal story and act it out, talk about friendly behaviour, sort groups of 10. → TG pp. 107–109

Connect

a Look. What is the panda doing?

b Colour the stars and the Moon.

At home

Talk with your child about how we relax before bedtime such as reading night-time stories and other routines.

In this session, children will also: find out where animals sleep, talk about bedtime routines, play an active game, make a night-time picture. → TG pp. 107–109

Grow, grow, grow

Life cycles

1

2

3

4

a Listen to your teacher and find the pictures.

b Retell the story.

In this session, children will also: find out about a butterfly life cycle, sing a song with actions, make a butterfly. → TG pp. 110–112

At home

With your child, look for bugs in the garden or in a park. What kinds of bugs are they? What are they doing?

Explore

a Look. What is happening in each picture?

b Colour the lambs and the grass.

c Count all the animals.

At home

Help your child make a photobook with pictures from birth to now with their name on the cover. Talk about how they have grown.

In this session, children will also: find out about the life of a sheep, talk about babies growing up, count and compare groups, make a model sheep. → TG pp. 110–112

a Look. What insect is this?

b Number the pictures in order.

In this session, children will also: find out about a ladybird life cycle, make a ladybird, count and compare groups of ladybird spots. → TG pp. 110–112

At home

Go outside and help your child to find any evidence of insects under leaves. How many insects can you find?

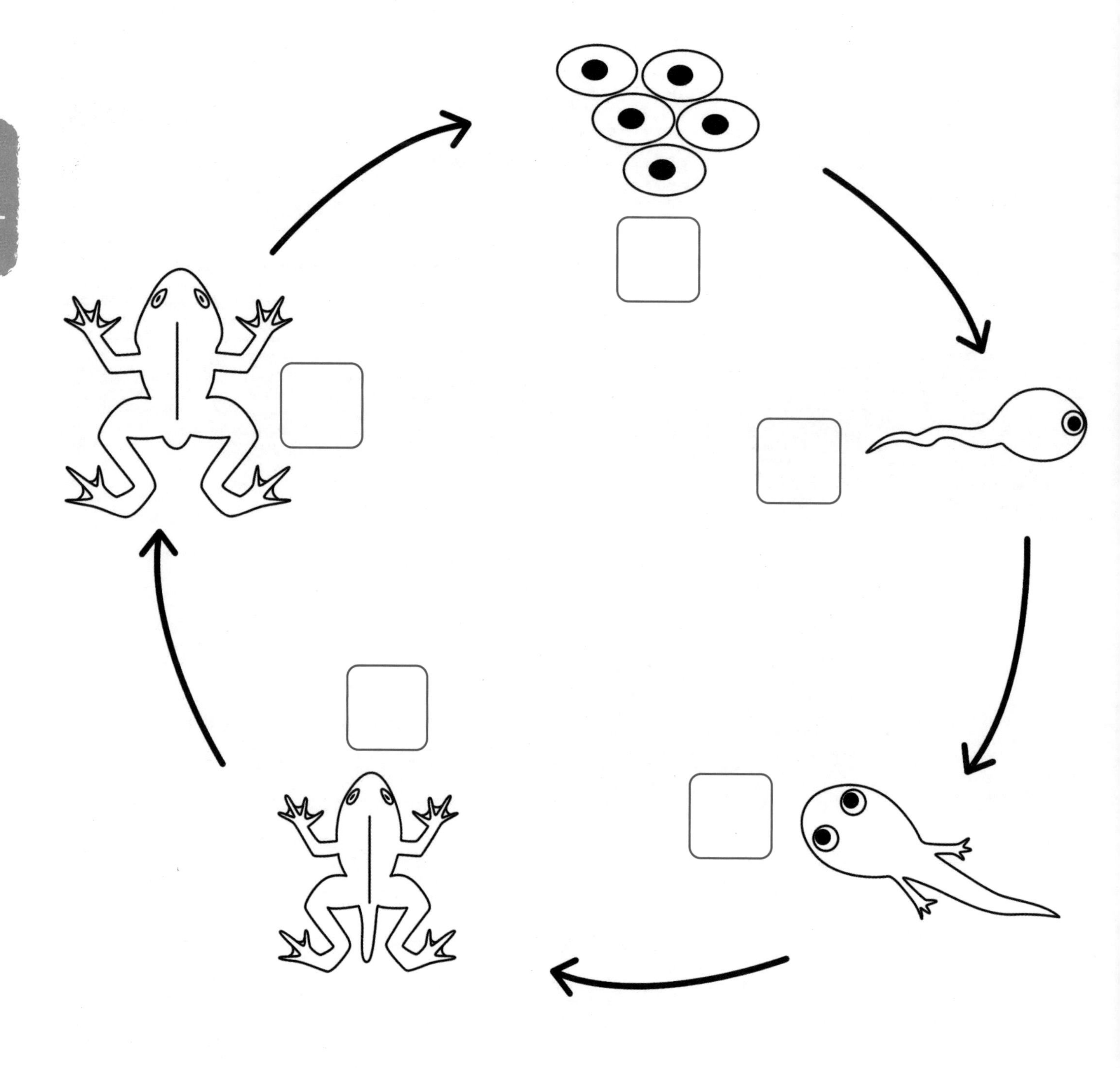

a Listen to your teacher and write in the correct numbers.

b Colour the pictures.

At home

Talk with your child about any babies that they know; encourage them to think about what babies do and what they need.

In this session, children will also: find out about a frog life cycle, review numbers 1–10, talk about life changes, explore a pretend pond habitat. → TG pp. 110–112

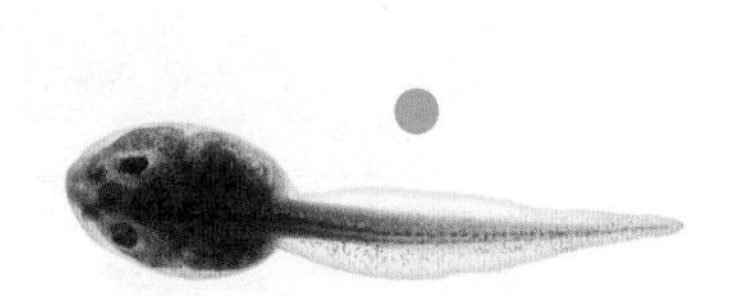

a Circle the smallest animal.

b Draw lines to match the animals to their habitats.

In this session, children will also: review habitats and life cycles, make and describe an animal model, compare groups, move like different animals. → TG pp. 110–112

At home

Go outside with your child and look out for birds and animals. Talk about the places where they live.

Book fun

In this topic, learners are encouraged to:

- recognize colours and the properties of simple shapes and use them in play
- join in with rhymes, songs, and poems
- identify rhyming words
- explore similar and opposite 'pairs'
- group and count things in sets.

Teachers will also help learners to:

- talk about favourite books and story characters
- use words to talk about time and memories
- use materials to model a craft plane
- retell favourite stories with different endings
- make up and perform a poem in groups.

My favourites

a Look. Where are the children?

b Listen to your teacher and trace the shapes with your finger.

c Find a book about birds.

d Say. What is your favourite cover?

At home

Read your child's favourite book together. Ask what makes the book special.

In this session, children will also: talk about choosing books, review simple shapes, share books and choose favourites, role play a library. → TG pp. 113–116

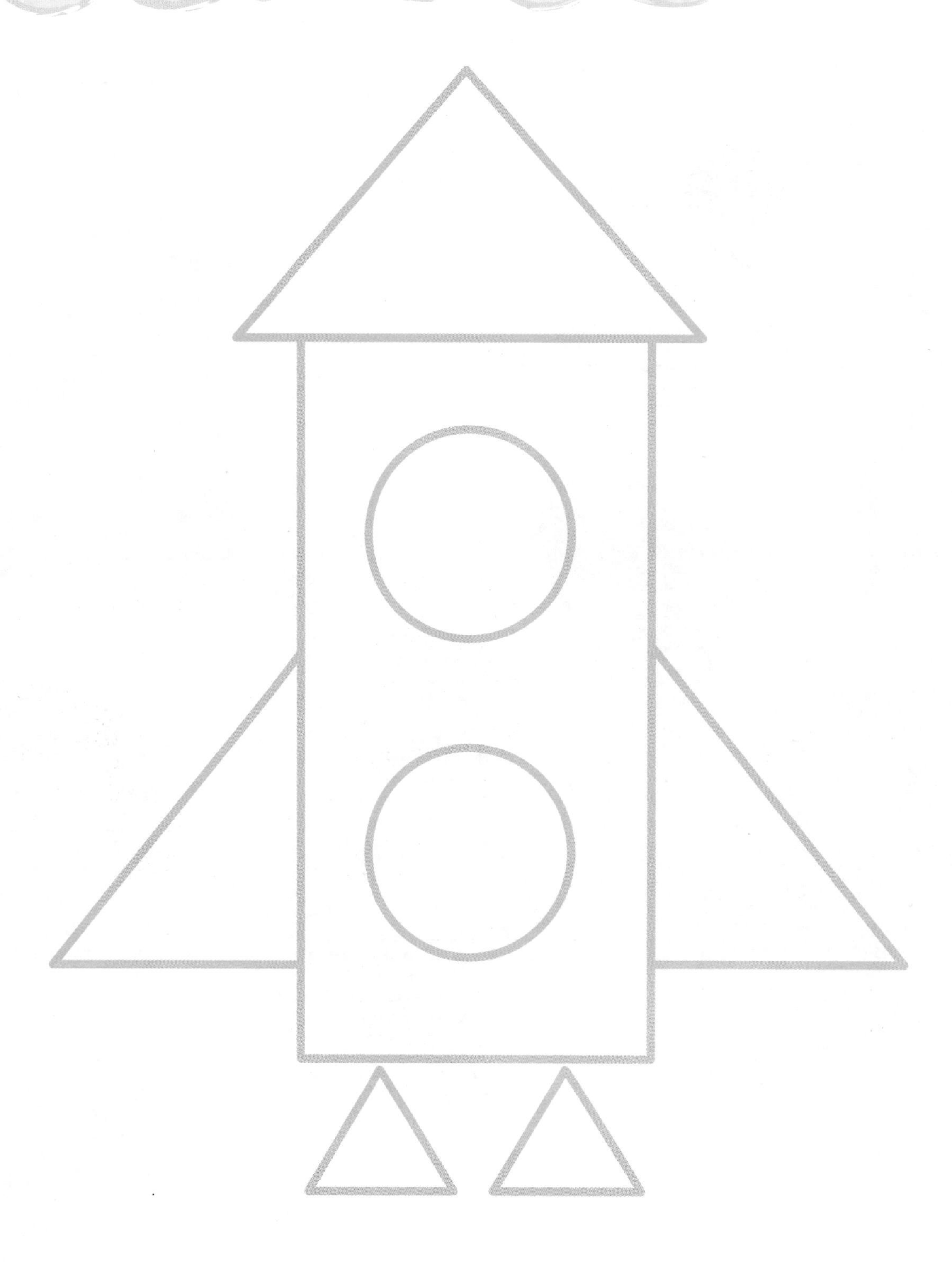

a Trace the rectangle.

b Listen to your teacher and colour the shapes.

At home

Choose a picture book and ask your child to help you find circles and triangles in the pictures.

In this session, children will also: name and count shapes, share stories set in space, make a model rocket, play 'musical shapes'. → TG pp. 113–116

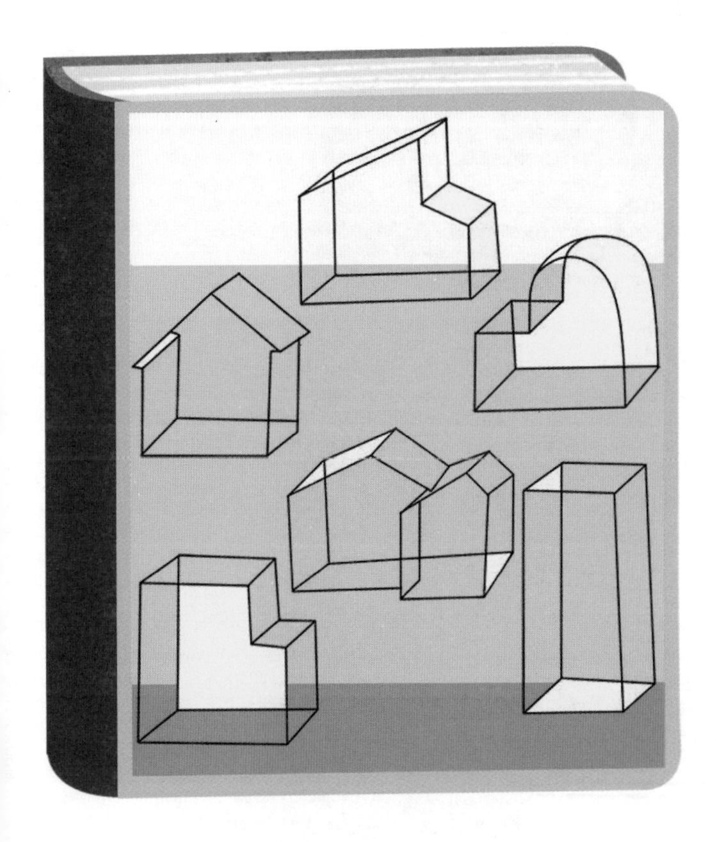

a Look. What are the books about?

b Find the shapes with straight edges.

In this session, children will also: spot shapes with straight edges, make a class memory book, make a track with curved and straight pieces, share food stories. → TG pp. 113–116

At home

With your child find kitchen items with straight edges (knives, boards, etc.) and those that have curves (bowls, spoons, etc.).

My favourites

a Trace the numbers.

b Draw and colour your favourite shape or shapes on the book cover.

At home

Draw some curved and straight shapes on some paper and support your child in cutting them out carefully.

In this session, children will also: vote for a favourite book, hunt for shapes in the environment, make a book about their favourite things. → TG pp. 113–116

a Colour the shapes.

b Draw your favourite character.
Say the shape.

In this session, children will also: make a stick puppet, invent shape characters, act out a story, count 10 objects and sort into sets. → TG pp. 113–116

At home

Talk to your child about what their favourite books, toys and foods are; talk about the reasons why they like them.

Storytime

a Find the characters you know.

b Count the animal costumes.

c Look. What shapes can you see?

d Sing The fairy tale song.

At home

Read your child a story that they know well. Work together to make a different ending.

In these sessions, children will also: listen to stories and choose favourites, talk about endings, practise naming shapes and counting to 10, make fairy tale houses. → TG pp. 117–119

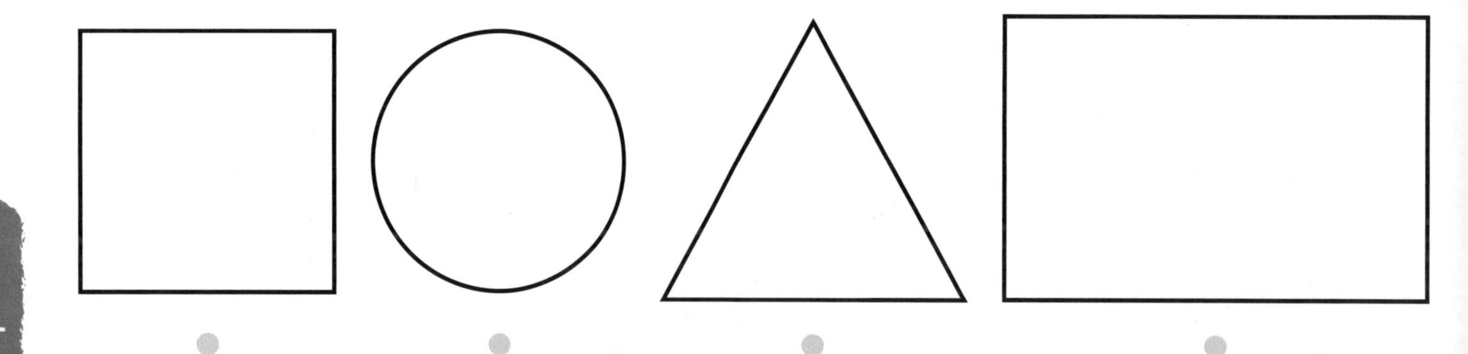

a Draw lines to match the shapes.

b Listen to your teacher and colour the clothes.

At home

Read fairy tales with your child and let them explore the pictures. What shapes can they find?

In this session, children will also: act out a story, revise shapes and colours, count and sort items into groups, make fairy tale character masks. → TG pp. 117–119

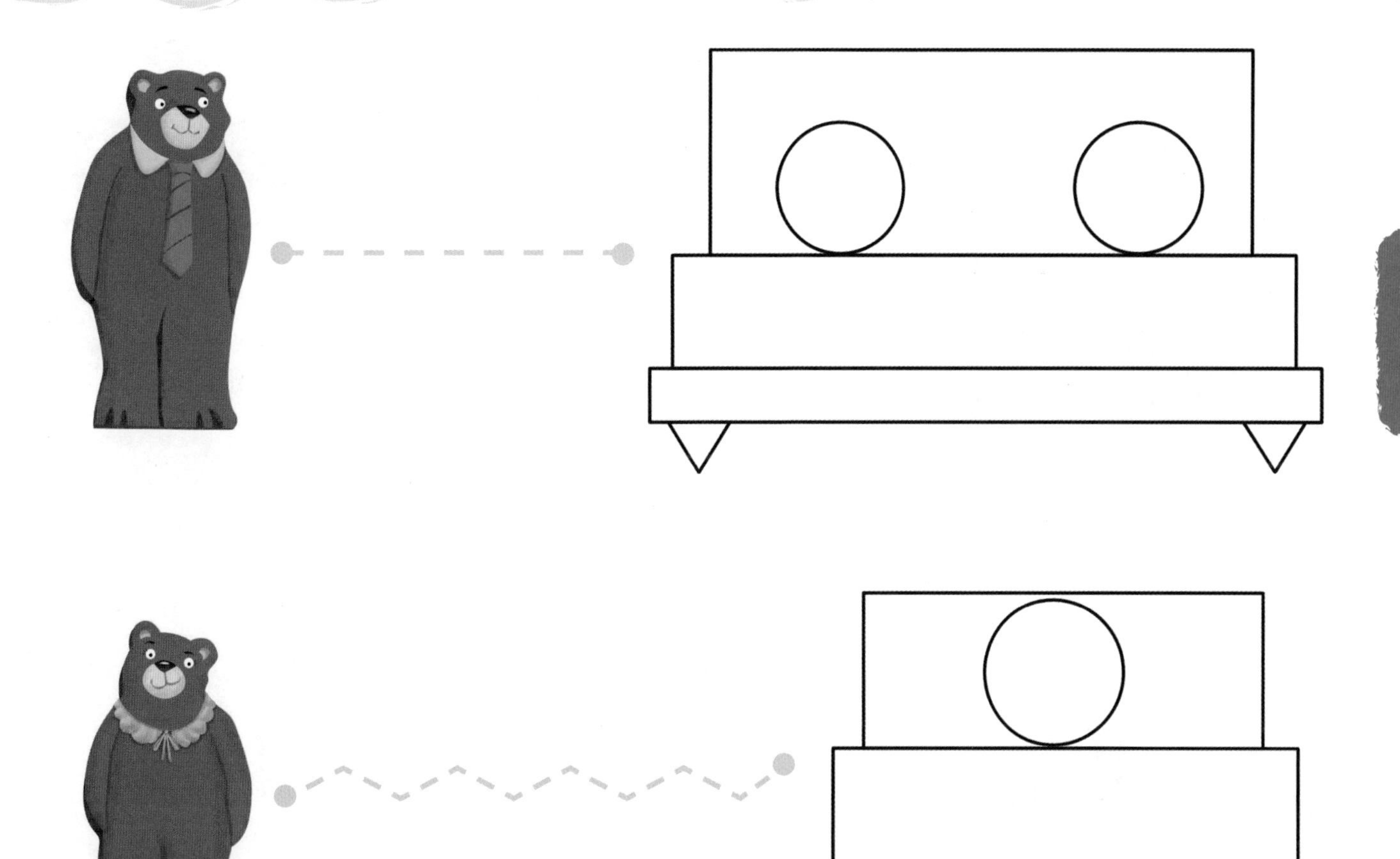

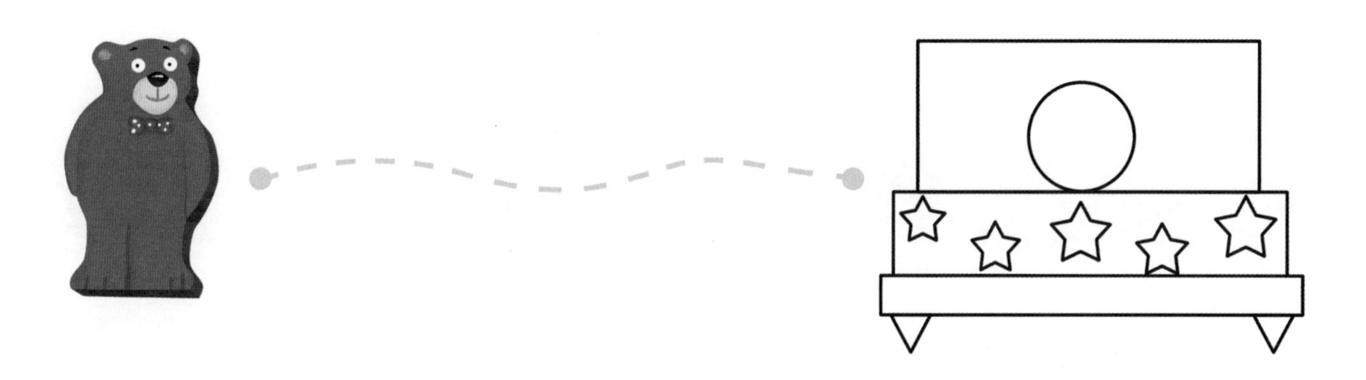

a Trace to help each bear find their bed.

b Colour the beds.

At home

Help your child chop fruit safely, cutting it up into small, medium, and large pieces.

In this session, children will also: retell 'The Three Bears', name and count shapes, identify opposites, make up stories about 3 characters. → TG pp. 117–119

a Draw in the faces. How do the characters feel?

b Circle the character that you think is brave.

At home

Talk to your child about being brave; ask them if they have been brave.

In this session, children will also: talk about being brave, dress up as their favourite characters, bravely try a physical challenge. → TG pp. 117–119

Go, stop, go!

a Look. What are the children doing?

b Practise the Go, stop, go! rhyme.

At home

Make up rhymes or read some and ask your child to clap every time you say the rhyming word in a pair (hat/mat; hen/pen; fun/sun).

In this session, children will also: listen for rhyming words in a game, fly paper aeroplanes, move around like different vehicles. → TG pp. 120–122

a Tick (✓) 2 animals.

b Cross (✗) the things that don't rhyme in each set.

At home

Make sets of 3 objects (2 similar, 1 different). Ask your child to spot the odd one out and give reasons.

In this session, children will also: join in with nursery rhymes and choose their favourite, find rhyming pairs. → TG pp. 120–122

small loud

tall

a Listen to your teacher and trace the rhyming words.

b Draw lines to match the words to the pictures.

In this session, children will also: match rhyming words and pictures, compare tall and small, try making the tallest tower, make rhyming words. → TG pp. 120–122

At home

Read out rhymes from your child's favourite books. Ask them to listen out for the rhyming words.

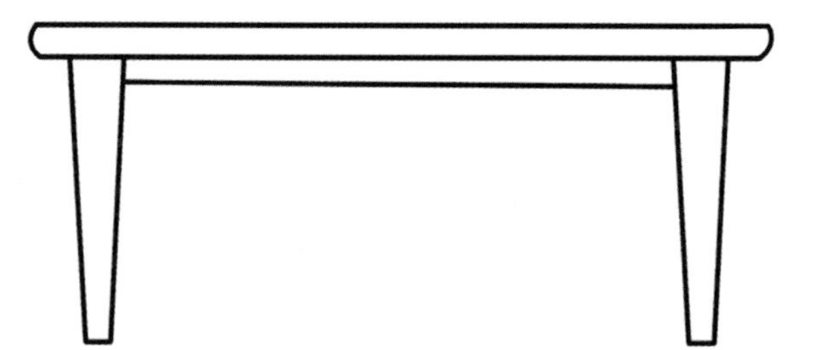

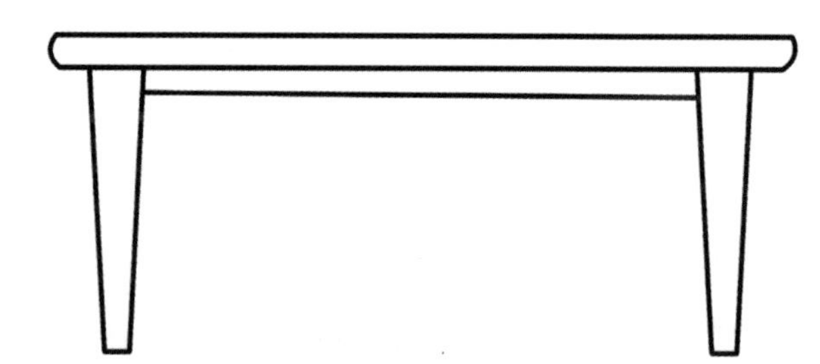

on top

under

a Draw what your teacher says.

on top

under

b Listen to your teacher and tick (✓) the rhyming words.

At home

Give simple instructions for your child to follow, using words such as *under*, *on top*, *behind*, *in front*. For example, '*sit under the table; put your teddy on top of the bed*'.

In this session, children will also: learn some prepositions, follow instructions to put toys in places, move to a beat, play a rhyming memory game. → TG pp. 120–122

a Colour 2 things that are **fast**.

b Colour 1 thing that is **high**.

In this session, children will also: talk about travelling, learn about road safety, practise saying opposites, make model vehicles with wheels. → TG pp. 120–122

At home

Share a nursery rhyme with your child; encourage them to spot the rhyming words.

Let's play!

a Say the numbers on the board.

b Look. What rhymes with **2**?

c Count the red beads. Count the blue beads.

d Chant Let's play, let's play.

In these sessions, children will also: find words that rhyme with numbers, join in with number rhymes, use numbers in play, recognize and draw their age number. → TG pp. 123–125

At home

Say a number word, such as '1'. Encourage your child to answer with a rhyming word, such as 'bun/sun'. Repeat with other numbers to 10.

Let's play!

Explore

a Colour 3 fish and 2 fish .

b Colour 4 fish and 1 fish .

In this session, children will also: count and compare groups, talk about water safety, share a story about a fish, make a magnetic fishing game. → TG pp. 123–125

At home

Give your child a set of 6 small objects. How many different ways can they split them into 2 groups? For example. 5 and 1, 4 and 2, 3 and 3.

Let's play!

a Circle the things that are the same.

b Count. How many things are there in total?

At home

Give your child a group of 7 small items in a bag. How many different ways can they sort them into groups, for example, colour/shape/size?

In this session, children will also: find rhyming words, perform a rhyme with actions, count sounds, count and compare groups of objects. → TG pp. 123–125

a Colour the things that rhyme.

b You are the author! Write your name.

At home

Look through picture books with your child and help them spot books that have the same author or illustrator.

In this session, children will: review their learning by joining in with rhymes, writing their name, sorting curved and straight-sided shapes, retelling a familiar story. → TG pp. 123–125

Growing bigger

In this topic, learners are encouraged to:

- make simple size comparisons using words such as 'taller, bigger, shorter, smaller'
- recognize, describe and create simple shapes
- retell and perform a simple story
- count, group, and describe things that are 'the same' and 'different'
- make up a story.

Teachers will also help learners to:

- write their own initials and begin to write their names
- use numbers 1 to 10 and talk about numbers with special meaning
- join in construction play using measurement and sharing tasks in a group
- explore the changes that happen to living things as they grow
- talk about their feelings and how to manage them.

Taller, stronger

Engage

a Look. Where is the baby?

b Name the shapes.

c Look at the children. Who is older?

d Listen to your teacher and count the people.

At home

Make family handprint art with your child, arranging the hands from small to large.

In these sessions, children will also: name and describe family members, fit shapes together, talk about changing from baby to child, make a frame for a baby photo. → TG pp. 126–129

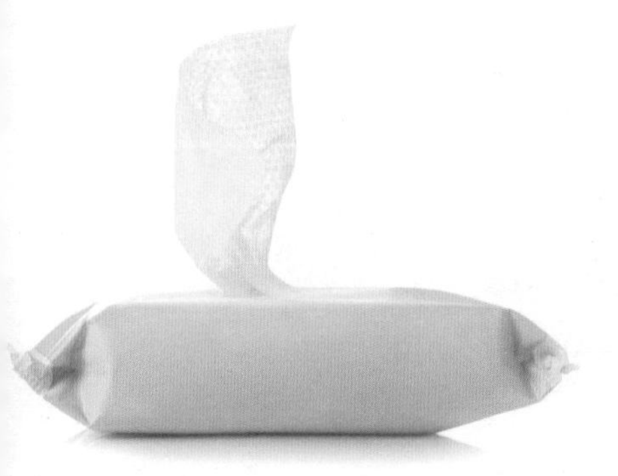

a Baby is going out. Cross out (✗) what we don't need.

b Draw lines to pack each item in the bag. How many are they?

At home

Look together at photos of your child at different ages. Help them explain what they can do at each age.

In this session, children will also: ask questions about looking after a baby, practise rolling, crawling, shuffling, talk about twins. → TG pp. 126–129

a Use string to measure the baby and the clothes.

b Tick (✓) the sleepsuit that fits the baby.

At home

Together compare your child's baby clothes to some they wear now.

In this session, children will also: order clothes by size, measure and compare sizes, use a height chart, find things they are taller and smaller than. → TG pp. 126–129

a Say the colour of the blocks.

b Look. Is the tower taller than the children?

c Look. How are the children feeling?
Colour the correct face.

In this session, children will also: work as a team to build a tall tower, paint pictures to show how they have grown and changed. → TG pp. 126–129

At home

With your child build a wall. Talk about working as a team.

Look at me!
Monday 8 May
Gibrai
G

a Sing Look at me!.

b Find Sam and his toy zebra.

c Look. What is Maya doing?

d Count the pompoms.

In these sessions, children will also: reflect on things they and the course characters have learned, look for numbers, practise writing numbers, practise yoga poses. → TG pp. 130–132

At home

Together make a labelled collage of the photos of all the 'grown-up' things your child does now.

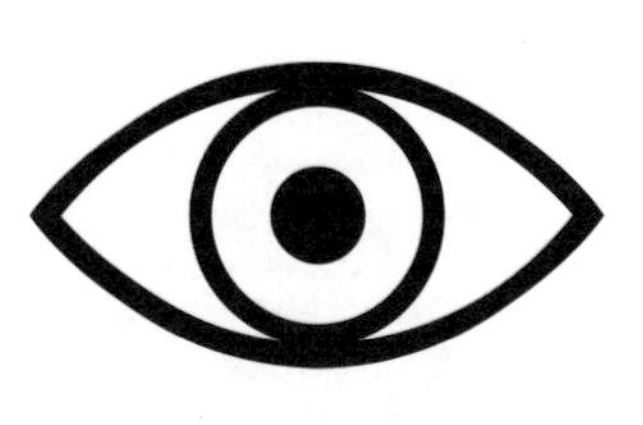

a Listen to your teacher and point to the parts of the body.

b Choose 1 picture. Say how you think it sounds, smells, tastes, or feels.

At home

Respond to your child's questions by asking *'How could we find that out?'* and use the internet together.

In this session, children will also: revise the five senses, make up their own questions, remember numbers 0–10, practise getting dressed. → TG pp. 130–132

a Look. How does each picture make you feel?

b Colour the pictures that are scary to you.

At home

Read a story to your child in which a character is brave, scared or both; discuss the feelings together.

In this session, children will also: talk about feeling scared, share a story about being brave, take part in an imaginary adventure story. → TG pp. 130–132

☐ •   • first

☐ •   • then

☐ •   • finally

a Number the pictures in order.

b Match the pictures with the words.

At home

Use opportunities to talk about hygiene; remind your child when they should wash their hands.

In this session, children will also: describe a new food using senses, follow instructions in order, learn about germs, make a hand washing poster. → TG pp. 130–132

We are special!

Our castle

1

2

3

4

a Listen to your teacher and count each shape.

b Retell the story.

In this session, children will also: listen to a story, build a castle together, make a self-portrait, dress up to act out a story. → TG pp. 133–136

At home

Together draw a tree for 'I am special' with branches for your child's characteristics.

______________'s castle

a Look and colour. Decorate the castle.

b Write your name.

At home

Celebrate your child being special; display photos and artwork, and talk about what makes them special.

In this session, children will also: compare characters, practise writing their name, decorate a picture in a unique way, look closely at thumbprints. → TG pp. 133–136

a Count and say the number of eyes in total.

b Look. How are they the same?

In this session, children will also: make model monsters, teach each other new skills, share monster stories. → TG pp. 133–136

At home

Show your child photos of family and friends; talk about what is different/ the same.

a Find the grown-up lions.

b Count the baby lions.

c Look. How are the lions different?

At home

With your child compare animal features that are the same or different in books or online.

In this session, children will also: compare heavy and light items, look for differences in a set of natural objects, share a story about being different. → TG pp. 133–136

a Trace the words.

b Mimic the children and close your eyes.

In this session, children will also: sing action songs, throw, count and compare numbers of beanbags, name body parts, practise relaxing. → TG pp. 133–136

At home

Ask your child to lie down and relax each part of their body in turn, starting with the toes, up to the muscles in the face.

One world

a Look. What is your favourite outfit?

b Say the People are special rhyme.

c Listen to your teacher and find the people.

d Find the jug with the most water.

At home

With your child choose a country to learn more about; make a collage about it using online images.

In these sessions, children will also: learn about special outfits and foods from around the world, make a banner, share stories from other cultures, practise pouring and measuring. → TG pp. 136–139

hot

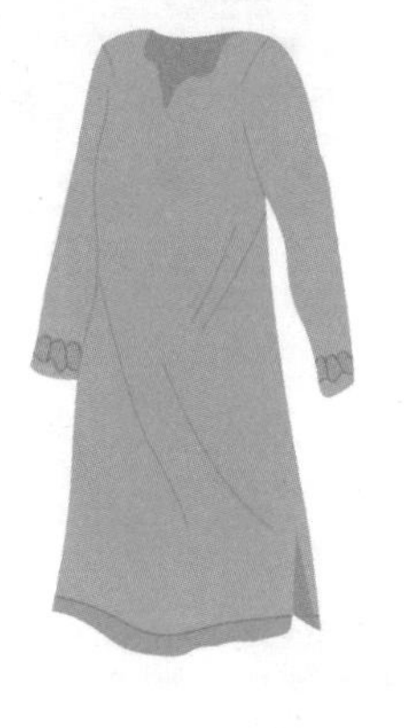

a Trace the words.

b Match the clothing with the weather.

At home

Help your child draw 2 outfits, for different types of weather, for their cuddly toy.

In this session, children will also: compare weather in different parts of the world, choose clothing for extreme weather, find out about a new place. → TG pp. 136–139

a Count how many animals have fur.

b Circle the pictures that go together.

In this session, children will also: compare animals living in hot and cold places, ask questions and find out more about animals, explore habitats. → TG pp. 136–139

At home

Encourage your child to find out about animals from your country; do a painting or a collage.

a Look. How are the fairy tale characters different?

b Choose some characters to make up a story.

At home

When reading stories to your child, help them compare the characters and their feelings.

In this session, children will also: review their learning by choosing story endings, finding opposites, measuring things, talking about feelings. → TG pp. 136–139